# Flying Solo Cello

Unaccompanied

folk and fiddle fantasias

for playing your cello anywhere

Book One

Myanna Harvey

Front Cover Image: Science, Industry and Business Library: General Collection , The New York Public Library. "Estampe anglaise de 1843 représentant l'aèroplane d'Henson dans un vol supposé aux environs de Londres." The New York Public Library Digital Collections. 1922. https://digitalcollections.nypl.org/items/627e815a-d992-c1e5-e040-e00a18062370

**A note about metronome markings: The tempo markings are suggestions only. These pieces may be learned and played at any tempo the player chooses. For the faster solos, there is no speed limit!**

CHP402



www.charveypublications.com - print books
www.learnstrings.com - PDF downloadable books
www.harveystringarrangements.com - chamber music

# Flying Solo Cello, Book One

all tunes arranged by Myanna Harvey

## Table of Contents

# Flying Solo Cello, Book One

**Note: Roman numerals refer to strings, not positions: I = A string II = D string III = G string IV = C string**

## Off She Goes

♩. = 76-104

Trad., arr. M. Harvey

**Lively**

36
mf
41
3 1 4
46
1
51
3
1 4 1
3 1
4 3
3 1
f
II
II
56
1 3 0 1
3 1
4 3 1
3
4
I
61
1
3
I
66
3 1 4
f
1
72
3
4 0 4 1
4
0

# Aura Lee

♩=84-104

G. Poulton, arr. M. Harvey

**Lyrically**

37
mf
41
II
f
45
mf
II
III
II
49
III II
f
54
59

# Sourwood Mountain

♩=116-160

Trad., arr. M. Harvey

**Lively**

33
37
41
mp
45
ff

# The Lark in the Morning

Trad., arr. M. Harvey

41
46
51
mp
56
f
61
mp
66
f
71
76
f

# Loch Lomond

Trad., arr. M. Harvey

♩=76-84

**Lyrically**

29
32
f
35
39
mp

# Staten Island Hornpipe

♩=104-132

**Lively**

Trad., arr. M. Harvey

mf
f
mf
f

# The Goat on the Green

♩. = 76-104

**Lively**

Trad., arr. M. Harvey

33
f
37
41
45
49
mf
II
I
53
f
57
61
ff

# Spring Breezes

Trad., arr. M. Harvey

poco rit.

# The Pennsylvania Quickstep

♩=126-152

Trad., arr. M. Harvey

mf
f
ff

# Down By the Riverside

♩=138-160

Trad., arr. M. Harvey

**Jaunty**

# Rising of the Moon

Trad., arr. M. Harvey

poco rit.

# Barbara Allen

♩=80-96

**Lyrically**

Trad., arr. M. Harvey

poco rit.

# The Miller of Glanmire

♩.= 76-104

Trad., arr. M. Harvey

**Lively**

33
37
p
41
fp
f
45
49
53
58
f
p
ff

# The Rakes of Mallow

♩=69-96

Trad., arr. M. Harvey

**Lively**

25
28
31
ff
34
p
37
ff

# Hard Times Come Again No More

♩=108-126

S. Foster, arr. M. Harvey

mp
f
mf
poco rit.

# The Connaughtman's Rambles

♩. = 76-104

Trad., arr. M. Harvey

36
41
46
f
50
54
mp
58
f
63
mp
68
f

# Waly, Waly

♩=92-108

**Flowing**

Trad., arr. M. Harvey

poco rit.

# Siman Tov

Trad., arr. M. Harvey

46
50
mf
55
59
f
64
mf
68
72
f
76
80
III
I
ff

# The World Turned Upside Down

♩=69-96

Trad., arr. M. Harvey

# Swing Low, Sweet Chariot

Trad., arr. M. Harvey

♩=104-120

**Feel free to swing some eighth notes:**

# Hungarian Gypsy Tune

Trad., arr. M. Harvey

♩=152-192

**Lively**

mf
f
accel.
p
ff

# When the Saints Go Marching In

♩=144-184

Trad., arr. M. Harvey

extend

2
Flying Solo Cello, Book Two
Haste to the Wedding
Lively
Trad., arr. M. Harvey
©2021 C. Harvey Publications All Rights Reserved.
3
©2021 C. Harvey Publications All Rights Reserved.

Made in the USA
Las Vegas, NV
15 September 2023

77602239R00031